Sticker Atlas

Dinosaurs

Book 1

Dinosaurs

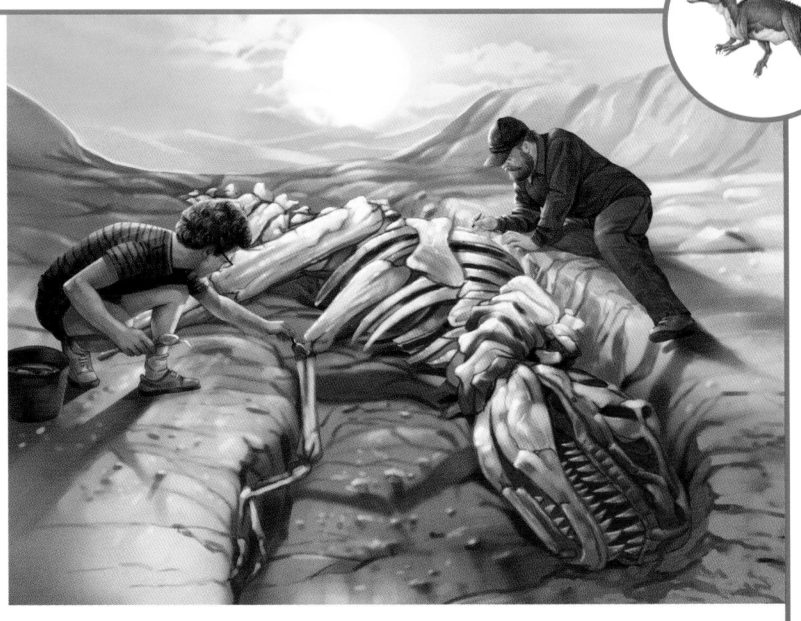

Dinosaurs were powerful prehistoric animals that lived on Earth for 160 million years, before suddenly becoming extinct 65 million years ago.

Dinosaurs were scaly, egg-laying reptiles, resembling the crocodiles or lizards of today. Dinosaurs included herbivores (plant-eaters) and carnivores (meat-eaters). Some dinosaurs stood on all fours (quadrupeds), while others were bipedal, standing on their two back legs.

Everything we know about dinosaurs comes from fossil remains such as bones, teeth and claws, which were buried and turned to stone over time.

Dinosaur scales have been found, but as all fossils are stone-coloured, it is impossible to tell what colour dinosaurs were.

Dinosaur families

Dinosaurs are divided into two groups, saurischia (saw·RISK·ee·a) and ornithischia (OR·ni·THISK·ee·a). The groups are distinguished by pelvis shape. Saurischians were 'lizard-hipped', while the ornithischians were 'bird-hipped'.

The saurischian group was made up of theropods and sauropods. Theropods were fast and ferocious bipedal carnivores. They included Tyrannosaurus (ti·RAN·o·SAWR·us).

Sauropods were large, long-necked herbivores. They included Diplodocus (di·PLOD·o·kus).

The ornithischian group was made up of all the remaining dinosaurs. Some stood on two legs and some stood on four. Many of them had plates, armour, horns or spikes to protect them from predators.

Saurischia: theropods **Saurischia: sauropods** **Ornithischia**

A changing earth

Since the formation of the earth, many plants and creatures have evolved and died out. Dinosaurs lived in the Triassic, Jurassic and Cretaceous periods. The first modern humans evolved less than 2 million years ago, in the Quaternary period, which we live in now.

During the time when dinosaurs ruled the world, the earth went through many changes. During the Triassic period, all the continents were joined together in one land mass we call Pangaea. The land started breaking apart and drifting during the Jurassic and Cretaceous periods, eventually dividing the earth into continents.

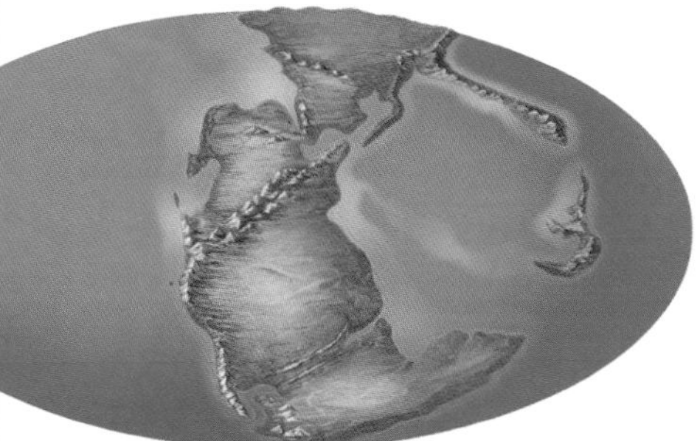

Triassic period

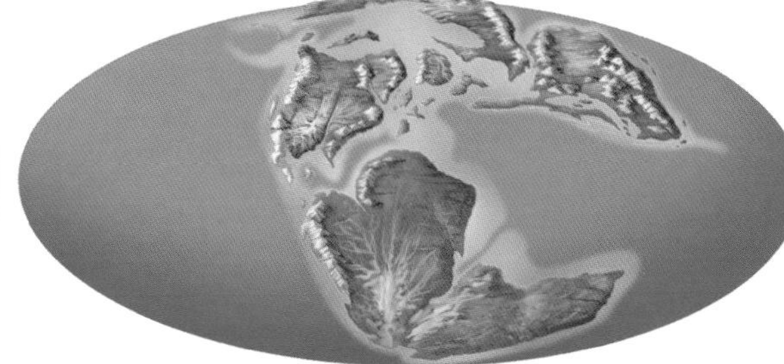

Jurassic period

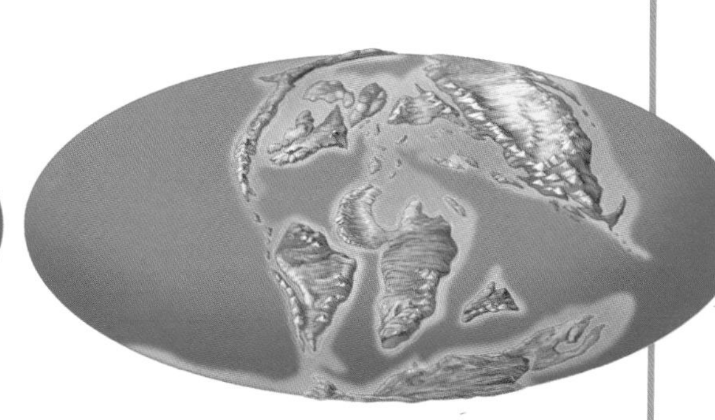

Cretaceous period

The evolution of dinosaurs

The first creatures to live on Earth inhabited the ocean. They were simple organisms such as seaweed, jellyfish and shellfish. Eventually there came to be fish, land plants, insects, amphibians and reptiles.

Before the coming of the dinosaurs, Earth was inhabited by prehistoric creatures, including massive reptiles.

Unlike most reptiles, dinosaurs stood on upright legs that were located straight under their bodies. Other reptiles, including lizards, had bent legs that came out of the sides of their bodies.

Legs of a dinosaur

Modern-day lizard

Triassic period

The Triassic period extended from about 250 to 200 million years ago. The earth was not divided into continents then as it is today, but was all one supercontinent that we call Pangaea, surrounded by an ocean we call Panthalassa.

The climate of the earth at this time was hot and dry. There was hardly any life on the land during the early Triassic period, with living things mainly occupying marine environments.

Eventually, marine creatures started to inhabit the land, and it is possible that dinosaurs evolved from these prehistoric reptilians.

Some of the earliest dinosaurs appeared in the mid to late Triassic period.

They included Coelophysis (SEEL·o·FIE·sis), a slender theropod that lived in North America.

It is possible that Coelophysis lived in packs, as many fossils of this dinosaur have been found together at Ghost Ranch in New Mexico.

A flock of Coelophysis

Late Triassic dinosaurs in the European region included the large plant-eating Plateosaurus (PLAT·ee·o·SAWR·us) and Liliensternus (LIL·ee·en·SHTER·nus), a small and speedy carnivore.

Pisanosaurus (pee·SAHN·o·SAWR·us) was an ornithischian plant-eater found in South America. It was hunted by Herrerasaurus (he·RER·a·SAWR·us), a small, fast and sharp-toothed theropod.

During the late Triassic period, as the first dinosaurs were evolving on the land, pterosaurs (TER·o·sawrs), the largest flying creatures of all time, inhabited the skies. Pterosaurs were not actually dinosaurs, but massive winged reptiles.

The exact appearance of Liliensternus is unknown – it might have been covered in scales or feathers.

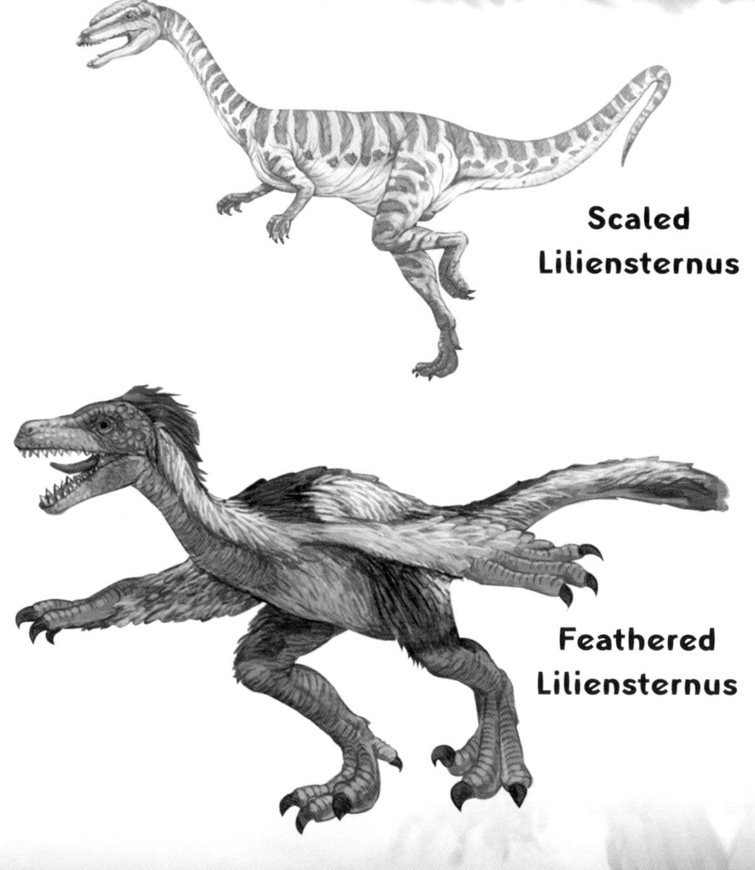

Herrerasaurus hunting Pisanosaurus

Jurassic period

The Jurassic period took place around 199 to 145 million years ago. During the early Jurassic period, Pangaea broke up into two supercontinents: Laurasia to the north and Gondwana to the south.

The climate on Earth was warm and wet, providing vegetation and allowing dinosaurs to thrive. Dinosaurs became larger and many more species evolved.

Laurasia

In Laurasia, there was an abundance of plants and many plant-eating dinosaurs, which meant that theropod predators had plenty of prey.

North America

Jurassic North America was home to many dinosaurs. Allosaurus (AL·o·SAWR·us) was a frightening theropod – a massive meat-eater reaching about 10 metres (33 feet) in height.

There were also giant sauropods such as Apatosaurus (a·PAT·o·SAWR·us), Camarasaurus (KAM·a·ra·SAWR·us) and Diplodocus (di·PLOD·o·kus), some of the biggest dinosaurs that ever existed.

It is estimated that Diplodocus reached around 50 metres (164 feet) in length.

Europe

In Europe, a 9-metre-long (30-foot) carnivore called Megalosaurus (MEG·a·lo·SAWR·us) reigned.

The late Jurassic period in Europe was also home to what scientists think was the first ever bird, Archaeopteryx (AHR·kee·OP·ter·iks).

Asia

Asia was home to Yangchuanosaurus (YAHNG·chwahn·o·SAWR·us), a horned theropod that preyed on sauropods including Mamenchisaurus (mah·MUHN·chee·SAWR·us) and Omeisaurus (UH·may·SAWR·us), as well as ornithiscian stegosaurs.

Gondwana

The new supercontinent of Gondwana was warm and flourishing, with plants providing plenty of food for animals, which were growing in size and number.

South America

Gondwana was home to large sauropods like the short-necked Brachytrachelopan (BRAK·e·TRAK·o·LO·pan). South America's sauropods continued growing and evolving, and by the Cretaceous period they were among the largest creatures to have ever walked the earth.

Africa

During the Jurassic period, massive dinosaurs appeared in Africa including the frightening theropod Ceratosaurus (se·RAT·o·SAWR·us), distinguishable by its horn, its massive jaws and predatory nature.

Kentrosaurus (KEN·tro·SAWR·us) was a stegosaurian similar to North America's Stegosaurus (STEG·o·SAWR·us). It was a spiky ornithischian living in the area of Tanzania, alongside massive sauropod Brachiosaurus (BRAK·ee·o·SAWR·us). Massospondylus (ma·so·SPON·di·lus) was a smallish, bipedal sauropod found in South Africa.

Cretaceous period

The Cretaceous period took place around 144 to 65 million years ago. During this time, the supercontinents of Laurasia and Gondwana broke up further, into the continents we have today.

Much of the land was covered by shallow water, and chalk rocks formed across the earth. The climate became cooler and seasons began. New life appeared, such as flowering plants, and with them, bees. Cretaceous Earth was also home to some of the first mammals and insects. The dinosaurs of the Cretaceous period were diverse and huge in size.

Quetzalcoatlus

Quetzalcoatlus, a flying reptile, had a wingspan of 12 metres (39 feet).

North America

During the Cretaceous period, North America was divided into islands because of high water levels. It was full of vegetation and flowering plants, as well as tall trees. In the sky was Quetzalcoatlus (KWET·zal·ko·AT·lus), the largest being ever to fly.

North American sauropods began to die out in the Cretacean period and were replaced by horned dinosaurs and hadrosaurs – duck-billed dinosaurs.

Edmontosaurus (ed·MON·to·SAWR·us) was one of the largest hadrosaurs, measuring about 13 metres (43 feet) in length, and it cohabited with the hadrosaur Parasaurolophus (PAR·a·saw·ROL·o·fus), which had a large crest on its head.

Triceratops (trie·SER·a·tops) was a massive plant-eating ornithischian that used its frill and three sharp horns to protect itself from predators such as Deinonychus (die·NON·i·kus) and Tyrannosaurus (ti·RAN·o·SAWR·us).

Deinonychus was a small theropod that possibly hunted in packs, and used the sharp claws on its feet as powerful weapons against its prey. Tyrannosaurus was a fearsome hunter, with massive jaws and teeth that it used to tear and devour prey.

Europe

Like North America, much of Europe was covered by shallow seas, and most Cretacean dinosaurs lived on the tropical islands that remained above water.

Baryonyx (BAR·ee·ON·iks) was a large carnivore that used its sharp teeth and hooked claws for hunting marine animals.

Iguanodon (i·GWAHN·o·don) was a bulky herbivore that could stand on two legs or on four. Close relations of Iguanodon were the duck-billed hadrosaurs, including Telmatosaurus (TEL·ma·to·SAWR·us).

Baryonyx hunting fish

Dsungaripterus

A Protoceratops and Velociraptor have been found fossilised in combat. Both dinosaurs died during the fight, probably due to a collapsing sand dune.

Asia

Asia was the largest continent in the Cretaceous period and was home to many living creatures. Massive reptiles such as Dsungaripterus (JUNG·gah·RIP·ter·us) dominated the skies.

On the land was Gigantoraptor (jig·ANT·o·RAP·tor), a large theropod that resembled a huge ostrich. Saichania (sie·KAHN·ee·a) was bulky and armoured, equipped with a club-like tail. Protoceratops (PROH·to·SER·a·tops) was a horned plant-eater about the size of a sheep. Velociraptor (vee·LOHS·i·RAP·tor) was a small, fierce theropod.

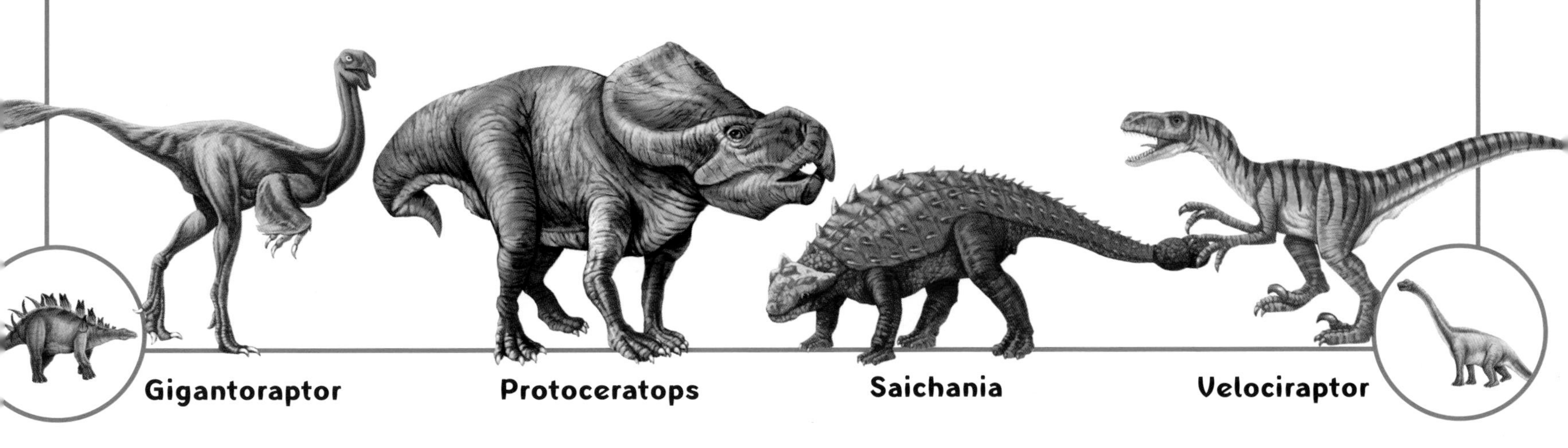

Gigantoraptor **Protoceratops** **Saichania** **Velociraptor**

South America

Saltasaurus (SAHL·tah·SAWR·us) and Rinconsaurus (RIN·kon·SAWR·us) were among the sauropods to inhabit Cretaceous South America. There was also Unenlagia (oon·en·LAHG·ee·a), a strange-looking theropod whose name means 'halfbird'. Giganotosaurus (jig·a·NOT·o·SAWR·us) was a giant carnivore found in Argentina.

Africa

Massive Spinosaurus (SPIE·no·SAWR·us), which had massive spines up to 2 metres (6.5 feet) long growing out of its back, ruled Africa, along with other carnivorous dinosaurs such as the giant theropod Carcharodontosaurus (kahr·KAR·o·DON·to·SAWR·us), with its massive jaws and serrated teeth.

There was also Deltadromeus (DEL·ta·DROHM·ee·us), another theropod giant, whose slender body shape and long limbs suggest it was a very fast runner.

Carcharodontosaurus means 'shark tooth lizard'.

Carcharodontosaurus

Oceania

Minmi (MIN·mee) and Muttaburrasaurus (muht·a·BUHR·a·SAWR·us) were Australian dinosaurs found around Queensland. Muttaburrasaurus was an ornithopod and Minmi was a very small, armoured ankylosaur.

Minmi

Deltadromeus

Jobaria

Lurdusaurus

Muttaburrasaurus

Extinction

All dinosaurs suddenly became extinct 65 million years ago, along with many other living creatures. This mass extinction is known as the Cretaceous–Tertiary extinction event.

There are several theories on why dinosaurs became extinct. Some scientists believe that it was due to the rapid change in atmosphere and climate that took place during the late Cretaceous period.

Others believe that Earth was hit by an asteroid or comet, which caused extreme temperatures that led to the extinction of most life on Earth.

Some believe that dinosaurs did not change their diet as the plant life changed, and so became extinct from lack of food.

The extinction event wiped out about three-quarters of life on Earth. Among the survivors were mammals. Much smaller than dinosaurs, these warm-blooded creatures were now free of the giant predators that had ruled Earth. Other survivors included the birds that now took over the sky, as the flying pterosaurs were all gone. Animals continued to evolve and diversify and eventually the earth became as it is today.

An icy Earth

How to use your giant wall map

Dinosaur fossils have been found all over Earth, and from these fossils we can guess where and when dinosaurs lived. The wall chart shows a map of Earth, divided into the continents as they are today. On the continents are spaces for you to place the stickers of dinosaurs and other creatures that lived in those parts of the world during the Triassic, Jurassic and Cretaceous periods.

Remember, the world was a changing place in the time of the dinosaurs and not all dinosaurs shared the earth at the same time. The stickers have the names of the creatures printed under them. Choose a dinosaur sticker, then look for a picture that matches that sticker on the map. Place the sticker over the picture and you're done!

Afrovenator
Avalonia
Alamosaurus
Dacentrurus
Acrocanthosaurus
Archaeopteryx
Albertosaurus
Liliensternus
Apatosaurus
Austrosaurus
Austriadactylus
Chirostenotes
Carcharodontosaurus
Gigantoraptor
Brachytrachelopan
Plateosaurus
Brachiosaurus
Atlascopcosaurus
Ceratosaurus
Allosaurus
Anchiornis
Deltadromeus
Camarasaurus
Dollodon
Edmontosaurus
Chialingosaurus
Chungkingosaurus
Iguanodon
Gargoyleosaurus
Giganotosaurus
Hypacrosaurus
Jobaria
Dsungaripterus
Kentrosaurus
Minmi
Megalosaurus
Parasaurolophus
Spinosaurus
Melanorosaurus
Protoceratops
Dimorphodon
Paralititan
Massospondylus
Probactrosaurus
Olorotitan
Pteranodon
Lapparentosaurus
Lurdusaurus
Muttaburrasaurus

Quetzalcoatlus
Rhabdodon
Saichania
Saltasaurus
Zalmoxes
Telmatosaurus
Rinconsaurus
Diplodocus
Stegosaurus
Velociraptor
Yangchuanosaurus
Pisanosaurus
Suchomimus
Tyrannosaurus
Triceratops
Diamantinasaurus
Australovenator
Unenlagia
Baryonyx
Wintonotitan
Herrerasaurus
Deinonychus
Coelophysis

Sticker Atlas
Animals

Illustrated by
Garry Fleming

Book 2

Animal Classes

Animal classes are groups of animals that are all alike in certain ways. Scientists have created these groups to make it easy to identify animals. The animal kingdom is divided into many classes, including mammals, birds, fish, reptiles, amphibians and invertebrates.

Mammals

The best way to tell if an animal is a mammal is to ask, 'does it have hair?' and 'does it feed milk to its young?'. If the answer to both of these questions is 'yes', it's a mammal.

Now, answer these two questions about the following animals: a human, a cat and a giraffe. Yes, they are all mammals. Some other mammals are dogs, elephants, lions, possums and mice, as well as around 5000 other types of animals.

Mammals can be found in virtually every part of the world. There are mammals that live on land, such as bears, monkeys and possums; mammals that live in the ocean, such as whales and dolphins; and even mammals that fly, such as bats.

Largest mammal: Blue whale, up to 33 metres in length

Smallest mammal: Bumblebee bat, 30–40 millimetres in length

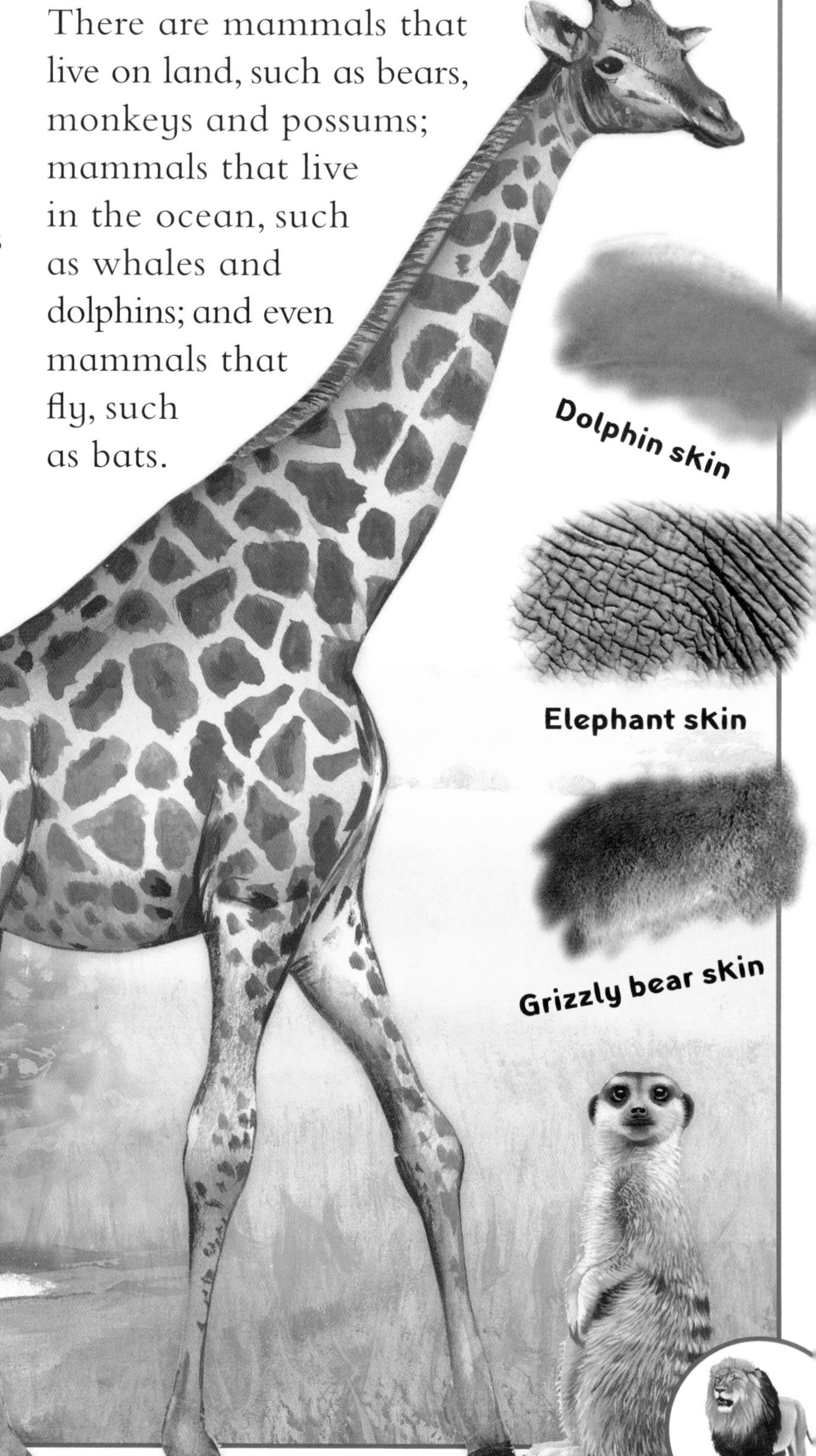

Birds

Birds are the only animals in the world that have feathers. Baby birds hatch out of eggs. A bird's wings and feathers make it able to fly, although some birds, such as ostriches and penguins, cannot fly.

Most birds are omnivorous, which means they eat both meat and vegetation. Some birds, such as sparrows and emus, eat fruit, seeds and small creatures including worms or insects. Some larger birds, such as eagles and vultures, eat other animals including mice, smaller birds or meat they find on animals that have already died.

Birds can be found on every continent on Earth: from emus in the desert plains of Australia, to the penguins in icy Antarctica.

Largest bird: Ostrich, up to 2.7 metres tall

Smallest bird: Bee hummingbird, around 6 centimetres in length

Fish

Fish are animals that live in water. All fish have scales, fins and gills. Gills are tiny slits in the side of their heads that allow fish to breathe oxygen from water. Some of the earliest fish, millions of years ago, did not have scales or jawbones.

There are many different and wonderful types of fish, from colourful reef fish, to sea dragons and sharks. Some fish, such as piranhas and salmon, eat other fish. Some fish, such as whale sharks and manta rays, eat mostly plants.

Fish can be found in most bodies of water on Earth, from lakes and rivers to oceans.

Largest fish: Whale shark, up to 15 metres in length

Smallest fish: Stout infantfish, up to 8 millimetres in length

Reptiles

Reptiles are cold-blooded animals that have scales. Because reptiles are cold-blooded, they rely on the sun to heat their bodies. This is why they can often be seen lying in direct sunlight. When their bodies become too hot, reptiles can lie in the shade or go for a swim to cool off.

There are thousands of different types of reptiles, from snakes and turtles to chameleons. Most reptiles eat meat including insects and small mammals, such as mice and rats, although some reptiles eat only plants.

Reptiles live on every continent except Antarctica. They live in all sorts of habitats, from deserts to rainforests and jungles.

Amphibians

Amphibians are animals that are born in the water and breathe through gills, but as they grow, they develop lungs and are able to live on land.

There are many different types of amphibians, but some of the most common are frogs, toads and salamanders.

Amphibians can be found in almost every part of the world, except in the Arctic regions.

Largest amphibian: Chinese giant salamander, up to 1.8 metres in length

Smallest amphibian: Brazilian gold frog, around 9.8 millimetres in length

Largest reptile: Saltwater crocodile, up to 7 metres in length

Smallest reptile: Dwarf gecko, around 6 millimetres in length

Invertebrates

Invertebrates are animals without backbones. They are by far the largest group of animals: more than 98 per cent of all animals in the world are invertebrates. Possibly the most well-known types of invertebrates are arthropods, which include insects, arachnids, molluscs and crustaceans.

Insects are creatures that have three body sections: a head, a thorax and an abdomen. Insects also have six legs and two antennae. Members of the insect group include ladybirds, beetles and dragonflies. Insects alone make up more than half of the known animal species on Earth.

Arachnids are creatures that don't have wings, have eight legs and two body sections. Members of this group include spiders, scorpions, mites and ticks.

Molluscs are animals that also have three body sections: a head, a middle section containing its organs and a foot to help with movement. Some different types of molluscs are snails, clams and octopuses.

Crustaceans are animals with hard outer shells that have two pairs of antennae. This group includes crabs, prawns and barnacles.

Invertebrates can be found just about everywhere on Earth, from icy-cold climates and hot, dry deserts to the deepest parts of the ocean.

Largest invertebrate: Giant squid, up to 18 metres in length

The Continents

Africa

Africa is the world's second largest continent. The northern part of Africa is made up mostly of desert, but the south is made up of fertile farmland, savannah grass plains and even jungles. This means a great many different types of animals call Africa home.

Animals such as ostriches, jackals, camels, foxes and scorpions can be found in the hot, dry north of Africa. Only animals that can survive on very small amounts of water can live in this area.

African elephants are the largest land mammals in the world. They can weigh over 5000 kilograms!

Animals that can be found in the grassy savannahs include giraffes, zebras, meerkats, gazelles and many other large herbivores that are able to travel across the plains eating the grass. In turn, these herbivores attract large predators, such as lions and leopards.

Animals that can be found in African jungles include gorillas, fruit bats, parrots, snakes and many types of insects.

Antarctica

Antarctica is the large frozen continent found at the very bottom of the earth. Antarctica is the only continent that does not have native people, but it does have some wildlife.

Animals that can be found in Antarctica include penguins, terns, a few species of arthropods such as mites and lice, and some marine animals such as whales, seals and sharks.

Antarctica is frozen all year round, and the average temperature is an icy minus 57 degrees Celsius, which makes it too cold for most animals to survive the harsh climate.

During the Antarctic breeding season, blue whales can eat enough food every day to feed a human adult for about four years!

Asia

Asia is the largest continent on Earth. It has a wide variety of landscapes and climates, from the snow and ice-covered mountainous areas in the north, to the lush tropical jungle, white sandy beaches and warm oceans in the south, and deserts in the west. This is why such a large number of different animals can be found in Asia.

In the snowy north, animals such as wolves, musk deer, reindeer and arctic foxes can be found. In the hotter, jungle areas animals such as elephants, orang-utans and many species of insects and lizards dwell. Fierce predators such as tigers and panthers also roam wild. Asia's most famous animal, the giant panda, lives in the central forest areas.

The name 'orang-utan' actually means 'man of the forest' in Malay. Orang-utans live only in small areas of Malaysia and Indonesia.

Oceania

Oceania is made up of many islands in the southern Pacific ocean. Oceania includes Australia, which is made up of warm, tropical regions in the north, deserts in the middle and west, and fertile farmland in the south. Even though it is the world's smallest continent, Australia is home to some of the world's oddest creatures. The wild dingo roams the bushy wilderness, frilled lizards bask in the desert and kookaburras laugh from the trees. Some of the world's most venomous snakes can be found throughout the continent, including the inland taipan and the tiger snake.

Perhaps Australia's most interesting animals are the marsupials. Marsupials are mammals that give birth to live babies at a very early stage of their development, and then the baby crawls up the mother's stomach and into her pouch where it begins to feed on milk. Some Australian marsupials are kangaroos, koalas and wombats.

Australian platypuses can eat their own bodyweight in food in any 24-hour period.

Europe

Europe is the world's second smallest continent. The north of Europe is made up of cold, icy regions, while the south has a warm, mild climate. Much of Europe is covered in farmland where pigs and cows are some of the most popular animals farmed.

Small mammals, such as moles and badgers, can be found throughout most of Europe. Large, predatory mammals, such as the grey wolf, are not so common, and can be found only in parts of western and northern Europe. This is because humans are now living on much of the land where these animals used to roam.

Europe is also home to many types of birds, including swans, ducks and quails.

North America

Like most of the continents, North America has many different types of landscapes and climates, which are home to many different types of animals.

At the top of North America, powerful grizzly bears can be found fishing for salmon from lakes and streams, while bald eagles soar high above the desert plains in the central regions.

Mountain goats and cougars roam the Rocky Mountains, and beavers build dams in the streams of forest areas.

Fossil remains show that millions of years ago, North America was probably home to the greatest number of dinosaurs in the world!

A hedgehog sheds its baby spines for adult spines. This is called 'quilling'.

South America

South America is a continent that has many wonderful and interesting animals. Much of the top half of the continent is made up of the gigantic Amazon Rainforest, which is home to thousands of animal species. Some of the most well-known animals that dwell in the Amazon are the sloths that live high up in the trees, giant anacondas and boa constrictors, brightly coloured macaws and big tarantula spiders.

The Andes Mountains are an enormous mountain range that runs along the western part of South America. Animals such as llamas, condors and pumas call these rocky regions 'home'.

The Galapagos Islands, which are located off the western tip of South America, are renowned for being home to many animals that do not live in the wild anywhere else on Earth. The most famous of these are the giant Galapagos tortoises.

Other animals that can be found in South America include armadillos, toucans, flamingos and capybaras. The legendary vampire bat is also a resident of South America.

Scientists believe that wild Galapagos tortoises can live for up to 200 years!

Exciting Animal Facts

Polar bears are the largest land predators in the world. The largest ever recorded polar bear weighed around 1000 kilograms!

Chimpanzees are the most closely related animals to humans. In fact, many scientists believe that we share around 98% of our DNA!

Scarab beetles were considered sacred in ancient Egyptian times.

Chameleons can change their skin to a variety of different colours! The change in colour depends on the temperature, the amount of light present and even their mood.

Capybaras are the world's largest rodents.

Scientists do not know for certain why flamingos sometimes stand on only one leg.

Giant pandas are highly endangered. It is believed that there are only about 1500 to 2000 still living in the wild.

Platypuses and echidnas are the only mammals in the world that lay eggs instead of giving birth to live young.

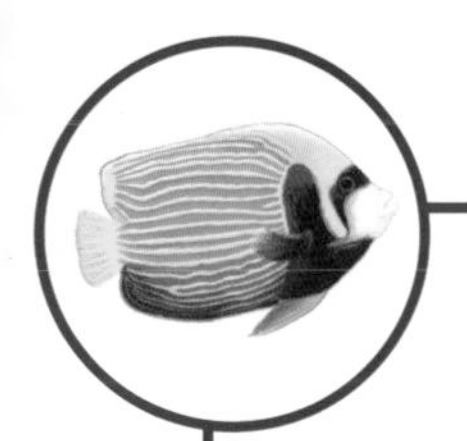

How to use your giant wall map

The wall map shows each of the world's six inhabited continents. Each continent is placed inside a box so that you can clearly see what countries are part of that continent.

On and around the continents are spaces for you to place the stickers of animals that live on that continent. The stickers have the names of the animals printed under them. Choose an animal sticker, then look for a picture that matches that sticker on the map. Place the sticker over the picture, and you're done!

Many animals live on more than one continent. For instance, wolves live in North America and Europe and badgers live in Africa, Europe and Asia. What other animals can you think of that might live on more than one continent?

Camel
Jackal
Crocodile
Hyena
Leopard
Ostrich
Lion
Giraffe
Scarab beetle
Vulture
Hippopotamus
Rhinoceros
Meerkat
Gorilla
Chimpanzee
Zebra
Lemur
Butterfly
Fruit bat
Galapagos tortoise
Macaw
Armadillo
Toucan
Flamingo
Sloth
Piranha
Aardvark
Tarantula
Boa constrictor
Capybara
Guinea pig
Red kangaroo
Platypus
Bullfrog
Kiwi
Dingo
Chameleon
Bird of paradise
Sheep
Koala
Cockatoo
Frilled lizard
Tiger snake
Ring-tailed possum
Quokka
Kookaburra
Echidna
Weasel
Chicken
Wombat
Dragonfly
Mongoose
Giant flying squirrel
Panda
Elephant (Asian)
Tiger
Black panther
Orang-utan
Peacock
Atlantic puffin
Yak
Badger
Ladybird
Komodo dragon
Donkey
Hermit crab
Reindeer
Arctic fox
Wolf
Cow
Toad
Fire salamander
Rat
Common crane
Squirrel
Duck
Mole

Polar bear
Coyote
Green tree frog
Atlantic salmon
Raccoon
Bobcat
Gila monster
Grizzly bear
Arctic hare
Mountain goat
Snowy owl
Eagle
Turkey
Opossum
Beaver
Chipmunk
Skunk
Penguin
Seal
Blue whale
Albatross
Killer whale
Dugong
Narwhal
Angelfish
Sea star
Great white shark
Pufferfish
Hammerhead shark
Whale shark
Manta ray
Clownfish
Sea turtle
Walrus
Pelican
Jellyfish
Dolphin
Sea dragon
Sea otter
Octopus